C000201661

Bassoon
Scales, Arpeggios & Exercises

for Trinity College London
exams from 2017

Grades 1-8

Published by
Trinity College London Press
www.trinitycollege.com

Registered in England
Company no. 09726123

Grade 1

Candidate to prepare *either* section i) *or* section ii) in full				
either i) **Scales & arpeggios** (from memory) – the examiner will select from the following:				
Scales: C (starting an octave above the lowest tonic) and F major A minor (candidate's choice of *either* harmonic *or* melodic *or* natural minor)	one octave	min. tempi: scales: ♩ = 56	tongued *or* slurred	*mf*
Arpeggios: C (starting an octave above the lowest tonic) and F major A minor		arpeggios: ♪ = 80		
or ii) **Exercises** (music may be used):				
Candidate to prepare 1a *or* 1b; 2a *or* 2b; and 3a *or* 3b (three exercises in total).				
The candidate will choose one exercise to play first; the examiner will then select one of the remaining two prepared exercises to be performed.				
1a. Contemplate	*or*	1b. Without Words	for tone and phrasing	
2a. Marching Off	*or*	2b. Shuffle	for articulation	
3a. Symmetry	*or*	3b. Eastern Twist	for finger technique	

i) Scales & arpeggios

C major scale (one octave)

C major arpeggio (one octave)

F major scale (one octave)

F major arpeggio (one octave)

A harmonic minor scale (one octave)

A melodic minor scale (one octave)

A natural minor scale (one octave)

A minor arpeggio (one octave)

ii) Exercises

1a. Contemplate – tone and phrasing

1b. Without Words – tone and phrasing

Grade 1 continued

2a. Marching Off – articulation

2b. Shuffle – articulation

3a. Symmetry – finger technique

3b. Eastern Twist – finger technique

Grade 2

Candidate to prepare *either* section i) *or* section ii) in full				
either i) **Scales & arpeggios** (from memory) – the examiner will select from the following:				
Scales: F major	two octaves	min. tempi: scales: ♩ = 66 arpeggios: ♪ = 92	tongued *or* slurred	*mf*
D minor (candidate's choice of *either* harmonic *or* melodic *or* natural minor)	to 12th			
G major E minor (candidate's choice of *either* harmonic *or* melodic *or* natural minor)	one octave			
Arpeggios: F major	two octaves			
D minor	to 12th			
G major E minor	one octave			
or ii) **Exercises** (music may be used).				
Candidate to prepare 1a *or* 1b; 2a *or* 2b; and 3a *or* 3b (three exercises in total). The candidate will choose one exercise to play first; the examiner will then select one of the remaining two prepared exercises to be performed.				
1a. Springtime	*or*	1b. Tempo di Valse	for tone and phrasing	
2a. Dinosaur Dance	*or*	2b. Vive la Différence	for articulation	
3a. Sphynx	*or*	3b. Semitonal	for finger technique	

i) Scales & arpeggios

F major scale (two octaves)

F major arpeggio (two octaves)

D harmonic minor scale (to 12th)

D melodic minor scale (to 12th)

Grade 2 continued

D natural minor scale (to 12th)

D minor arpeggio (to 12th)

G major scale (one octave)

G major arpeggio (one octave)

E harmonic minor scale (one octave)

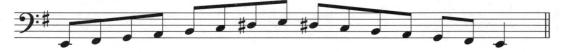

E melodic minor scale (one octave)

E natural minor scale (one octave)

E minor arpeggio (one octave)

ii) Exercises

1a. Springtime – tone and phrasing

1b. Tempo di Valse – tone and phrasing

2a. Dinosaur Dance – articulation

Grade 2 continued

2b. Vive la Différence – articulation

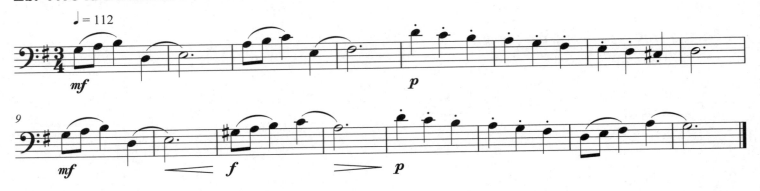

3a. Sphynx – finger technique

3b. Semitonal – finger technique

Grade 3

Candidate to prepare *either* section i) *or* section ii) in full				
either i) **Scales & arpeggios** (from memory) – the examiner will select from the following:				
Scales: C and G major	two octaves	min. tempi: scales: ♩ = 72 arpeggios: ♪ = 100	tongued *or* slurred	*mf*
B♭ major (starting an octave above the lowest tonic) A minor (candidate's choice of *either* harmonic *or* melodic minor)	to 12th			
G minor (candidate's choice of *either* harmonic *or* melodic minor)	one octave			
Chromatic scale starting on G				
Arpeggios: C and G major	two octaves			
B♭ major (starting an octave above the lowest tonic) A minor	to 12th			
G minor	one octave			
or ii) **Exercises** (music may be used):				
Candidate to prepare 1a *or* 1b; 2a *or* 2b; and 3a *or* 3b (three exercises in total). The candidate will choose one exercise to play first; the examiner will then select one of the remaining two prepared exercises to be performed.				
1a. Whistling a Tune	*or*	1b. Balance	for tone and phrasing	
2a. Hot and Cold	*or*	2b. Folksy	for articulation	
3a. Chromatic Dance	*or*	3b. Sunshine	for finger technique	

i) Scales & arpeggios

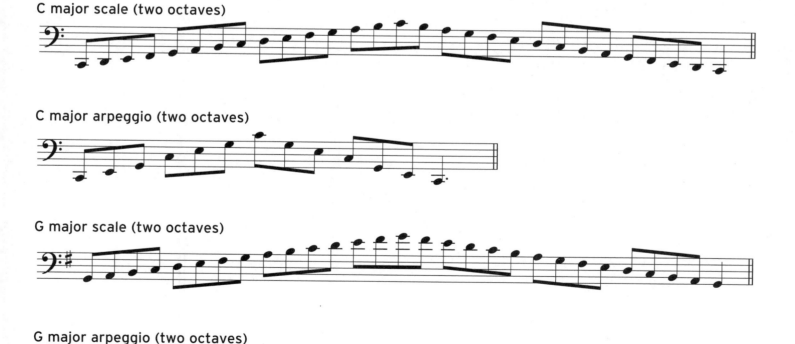

C major scale (two octaves)

C major arpeggio (two octaves)

G major scale (two octaves)

G major arpeggio (two octaves)

Grade 3 continued

Bb major scale (to 12th)

Bb major arpeggio (to 12th)

A harmonic minor scale (to 12th)

A melodic minor scale (to 12th)

A minor arpeggio (to 12th)

G harmonic minor scale (one octave)

G melodic minor scale (one octave)

G minor arpeggio (one octave)

Chromatic scale starting on G (one octave)

ii) Exercises

1a. Whistling a Tune – tone and phrasing

1b. Balance – tone and phrasing

2a. Hot and Cold – articulation

Grade 3 continued

2b. Folksy – articulation

3a. Chromatic Dance – finger technique

3b. Sunshine – finger technique

Grade 4

Candidate to prepare *either* section i) *or* section ii) in full					
***either* i) Scales & arpeggios** (from memory) – the examiner will select from the following:					
Scales: A♭, D and E♭ major G, B and C minor (candidate's choice of *either* harmonic *or* melodic minor)		two octaves	min. tempi: scales: ♩ = 80 arpeggios: ♪ = 120 7ths: ♩ = 69	tongued *or* slurred	*mf*
Chromatic scale starting on F					
Pentatonic (major) scale starting on F		one octave			
Arpeggios: A♭, D and E♭ major G, B and C minor		two octaves			
Dominant 7th in the key of C					
***or* ii) Exercises** (music may be used):					
Candidate to prepare 1a *or* 1b; 2a *or* 2b; and 3a *or* 3b (three exercises in total). The candidate will choose one exercise to play first; the examiner will then select one of the remaining two prepared exercises to be performed.					
1a. Semplice	*or*	1b. Melodie	for tone and phrasing		
2a. Q & A	*or*	2b. Scat	for articulation		
3a. Handy	*or*	3b. At the Ball	for finger technique		

i) Scales & arpeggios

A♭ major scale (two octaves)

A♭ major arpeggio (two octaves)

D major scale (two octaves)

D major arpeggio (two octaves)

Grade 4 continued

Eb major scale (two octaves)

Eb major arpeggio (two octaves)

G harmonic minor scale (two octaves)

G melodic minor scale (two octaves)

G minor arpeggio (two octaves)

B harmonic minor scale (two octaves)

B melodic minor scale (two octaves)

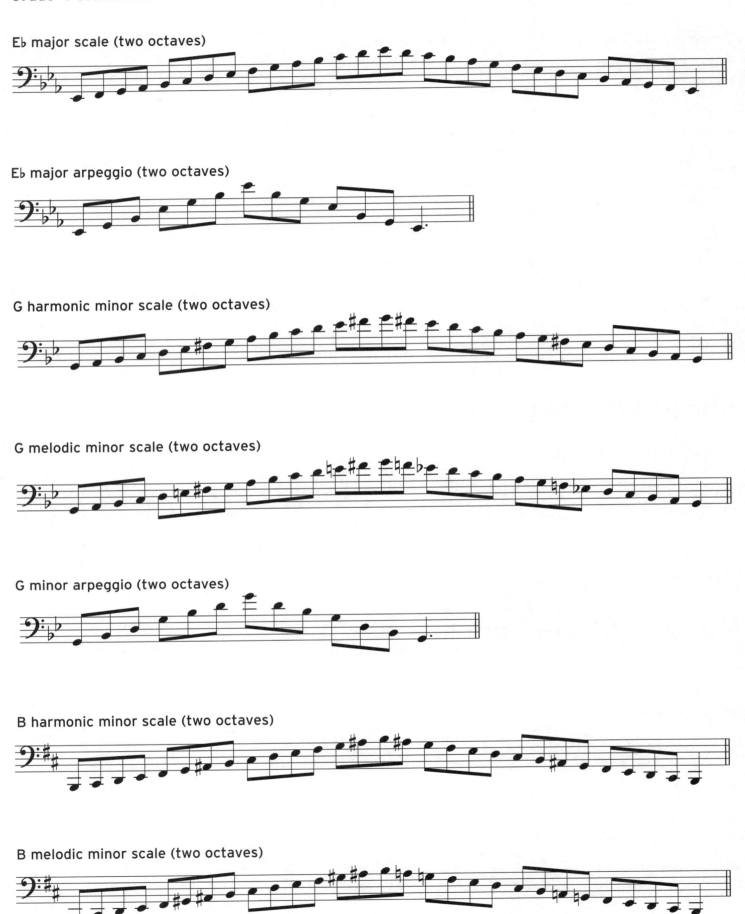

B minor arpeggio (two octaves)

C harmonic minor scale (two octaves)

C melodic minor scale (two octaves)

C minor arpeggio (two octaves)

Chromatic scale starting on F (two octaves)

Pentatonic (major) scale starting on F (one octave)

Dominant 7th in the key of C (two octaves)

ii) Exercises

1a. Semplice − tone and phrasing

1b. Melodie − tone and phrasing

2a. Q & A – articulation

2b. Scat – articulation

Grade 4 continued

3a. Handy – finger technique

3b. At the Ball – finger technique

Grade 5

Candidate to prepare *either* section i) *or* section ii) in full					
either i) **Scales & arpeggios** (from memory) – the examiner will select from the following:					
Scales: A, B♭ (candidates may start on the lowest tonic or an octave higher), E♭ and E major A, G, C and F♯ minor (candidate's choice of *either* harmonic *or* melodic minor)		two octaves	min. tempi: scales: ♩ = 92 arpeggios: ♪ = 132 7ths: ♩ = 76	tongued *or* slurred	*mf*
Chromatic scale starting on A Pentatonic (major) scale starting on C					
Arpeggios: A, B♭ (candidates may start on the lowest tonic or an octave higher), E♭ and E major A, G, C and F♯ minor					
Dominant 7th in the keys of B♭ and D Diminished 7th starting on E					
or ii) **Exercises** (music may be used):					
Candidate to prepare 1a *or* 1b; 2a *or* 2b; and 3a *or* 3b (three exercises in total).					
The candidate will choose one exercise to play first; the examiner will then select one of the remaining two prepared exercises to be performed.					
1a. Lilt	*or*	1b. Just a Minuet	for tone and phrasing		
2a. A Conversation	*or*	2b. Chase Away	for articulation		
3a. Gliding	*or*	3b. Seven Up	for finger technique		

i) Scales & arpeggios

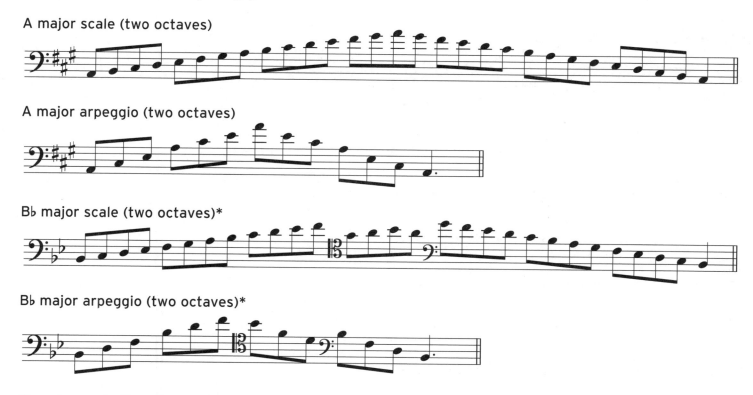

A major scale (two octaves)

A major arpeggio (two octaves)

B♭ major scale (two octaves)*

B♭ major arpeggio (two octaves)*

E♭ major scale (two octaves) – see Grade 4 page 14

E♭ major arpeggio (two octaves) – see Grade 4 page 14

* may also be played an octave lower

Grade 5 continued

E major scale (two octaves)

E major arpeggio (two octaves)

A harmonic minor scale (two octaves)

A melodic minor scale (two octaves)

A minor arpeggio (two octaves)

G harmonic minor scale (two octaves) – see Grade 4 page 14

G melodic minor scale (two octaves) – see Grade 4 page 14

G minor arpeggio (two octaves) – see Grade 4 page 14

C harmonic minor scale (two octaves) – see Grade 4 page 15

C melodic minor scale (two octaves) – see Grade 4 page 15

C minor arpeggio (two octaves) – see Grade 4 page 15

F# harmonic minor scale (two octaves)

F# melodic minor scale (two octaves)

F# minor arpeggio (two octaves)

Chromatic scale starting on A (two octaves)

Pentatonic (major) scale starting on C (two octaves)

Dominant 7th in the key of B♭ (two octaves)

Dominant 7th in the key of D (two octaves)

Diminished 7th starting on E (two octaves)

ii) Exercises

1a. Lilt – tone and phrasing

1b. Just a Minuet – tone and phrasing

2a. A Conversation – articulation

2b. Chase Away – articulation

Grade 5 continued

3a. Gliding – finger technique

3b. Seven Up – finger technique

Grade 6

Candidate to prepare *either* section i) *or* section ii) in full				
either **i) Scales & arpeggios** (from memory) − the examiner will select from the following:				
Candidates should prepare scales and arpeggios from the following tonal centres: Bb major, Bb minor	three octaves	min. tempi: scales: ♩ = 108 arpeggios: ♩. = 60 7ths: ♩. = 90	tongued, slurred *or* staccato-tongued	*f or p*
F major, F minor G major, G minor	two octaves			
Plus: Chromatic scale starting on Bb Dominant 7th in the key of Eb Diminished 7th starting on Bb	three octaves			
Whole-tone scale starting on G Pentatonic (major) scale starting on G	two octaves			

When the examiner requests a **major tonal centre**, the candidate should play in succession:
 	
   The major scale
   The major arpeggio
 	
When the examiner requests a **minor tonal centre**, the candidate should play in succession:
 	
   The melodic minor scale
   The harmonic minor scale
   The minor arpeggio				

or **ii) Orchestral extracts**				
See current syllabus for details.				

i) Scales & arpeggios

Bb major scale (three octaves)

Bb major arpeggio (three octaves)

Bb melodic minor scale (three octaves)

Grade 6 continued

Bb harmonic minor scale (three octaves)

Bb minor arpeggio (three octaves)

F major scale (two octaves) – see Grade 2 page 5

F major arpeggio (two octaves) – see Grade 2 page 5

F melodic minor scale (two octaves)

F harmonic minor scale (two octaves)

F minor arpeggio (two octaves)

G major scale (two octaves) – see Grade 3 page 9

G major arpeggio (two octaves) – see Grade 3 page 9

G melodic minor scale (two octaves) – see Grade 4 page 14

G harmonic minor scale (two octaves) – see Grade 4 page 14

G minor arpeggio (two octaves) – see Grade 4 page 14

Chromatic scale starting on B♭ (three octaves)

Dominant 7th in the key of E♭ (three octaves)

Diminished 7th starting on B♭ (three octaves)

Whole-tone scale starting on G (two octaves)

Pentatonic (major) scale starting on G (two octaves)

Grade 7

Candidate to prepare *either* section i) *or* section ii) in full				
either i) **Scales & arpeggios** (from memory) – the examiner will select from the following:				
Candidates should prepare scales and arpeggios from the following tonal centres: C major, C minor	three octaves			
E♭ major, E♭ minor D♭ major, C# minor A major, A minor	two octaves	min. tempi: scales: ♩ = 120 arpeggios: ♩. = 66 7ths: ♩ = 96	tongued, slurred *or* staccato- tongued	*f* or *p*
Plus: Chromatic scale starting on C Dominant 7th in the key of F Diminished 7th starting on C	three octaves			
Whole-tone scale starting on A Pentatonic (major) scales starting on A and E♭ Dominant 7th in the key of A♭ Augmented arpeggio starting on G	two octaves			

When the examiner requests a **major tonal centre**, the candidate should play in succession:
 	
   The major scale
   The major arpeggio
 	
When the examiner requests a **minor tonal centre**, the candidate should play in succession:
 	
   The melodic minor scale
   The harmonic minor scale
   The minor arpeggio				

or ii) **Orchestral extracts**				
See current syllabus for details.				

i) Scales & arpeggios

C major scale (three octaves)

C major arpeggio (three octaves)

C melodic minor scale (three octaves)

C harmonic minor scale (three octaves)

C minor arpeggio (three octaves)

Eb major scale (two octaves) – see Grade 4 page 14

Eb major arpeggio (two octaves) – see Grade 4 page 14

Eb melodic minor scale (two octaves)

Eb harmonic minor scale (two octaves)

Eb minor arpeggio (two octaves)

Grade 7 continued

Db major scale (two octaves)

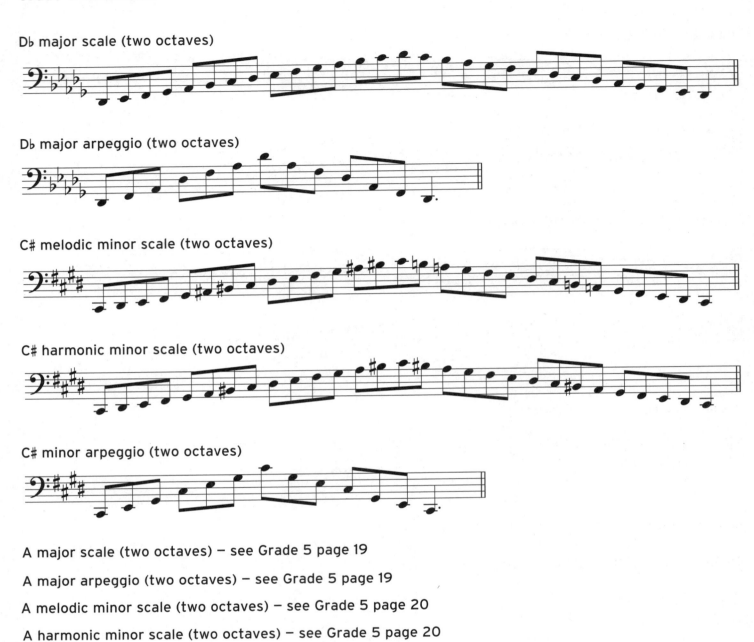

Db major arpeggio (two octaves)

C# melodic minor scale (two octaves)

C# harmonic minor scale (two octaves)

C# minor arpeggio (two octaves)

A major scale (two octaves) – see Grade 5 page 19

A major arpeggio (two octaves) – see Grade 5 page 19

A melodic minor scale (two octaves) – see Grade 5 page 20

A harmonic minor scale (two octaves) – see Grade 5 page 20

A minor arpeggio (two octaves) – see Grade 5 page 20

Chromatic scale starting on C (three octaves)

Dominant 7th in the key of F (three octaves)

Diminished 7th starting on C (three octaves)

Whole-tone scale starting on A (two octaves)

Pentatonic (major) scale starting on A (two octaves)

Pentatonic (major) scale starting on E♭ (two octaves)

Dominant 7th in the key of A♭ (two octaves)

Augmented arpeggio starting on G (two octaves)

Grade 8

Candidate to prepare *either* section i) *or* section ii) in full				
either i) **Scales & arpeggios** (from memory) – the examiner will select from the following:				
Candidates should prepare scales and arpeggios from the following tonal centres: B major, B minor D major, D minor	three octaves	min. tempi: scales: ♩ = 132 arpeggios: ♩ = 69 7ths: ♩ = 104	tongued, slurred, staccato- tongued *or* mixed articulation*	*f* or *p*
F♯ major, F♯ minor E major, E minor A♭ major, G♯ minor	two octaves			
Plus: Chromatic scale starting on D Dominant 7th in the key of G	three octaves			
Whole-tone scale starting on B Pentatonic (major) scale starting on B Dominant 7th in the key of B Diminished 7ths starting on B and F♯ Augmented arpeggios starting on F♯ and A♭	two octaves			

When the examiner requests a **major tonal centre**, the candidate should play in succession:
 	
  The major scale
  The major arpeggio
 	
When the examiner requests a **minor tonal centre**, the candidate should play in succession:
 	
  The melodic minor scale
  The harmonic minor scale
  The minor arpeggio				

or ii) **Orchestral extracts**				
See current syllabus for details.				

*Mixed articulation scales and arpeggios to be prepared with the following articulation:

i) Scales & arpeggios

B major scale (three octaves)

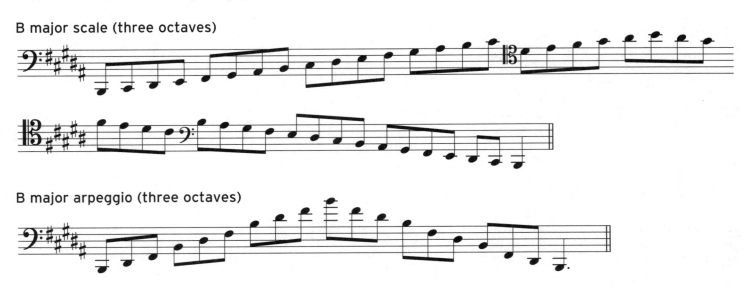

B major arpeggio (three octaves)

B melodic minor scale (three octaves)

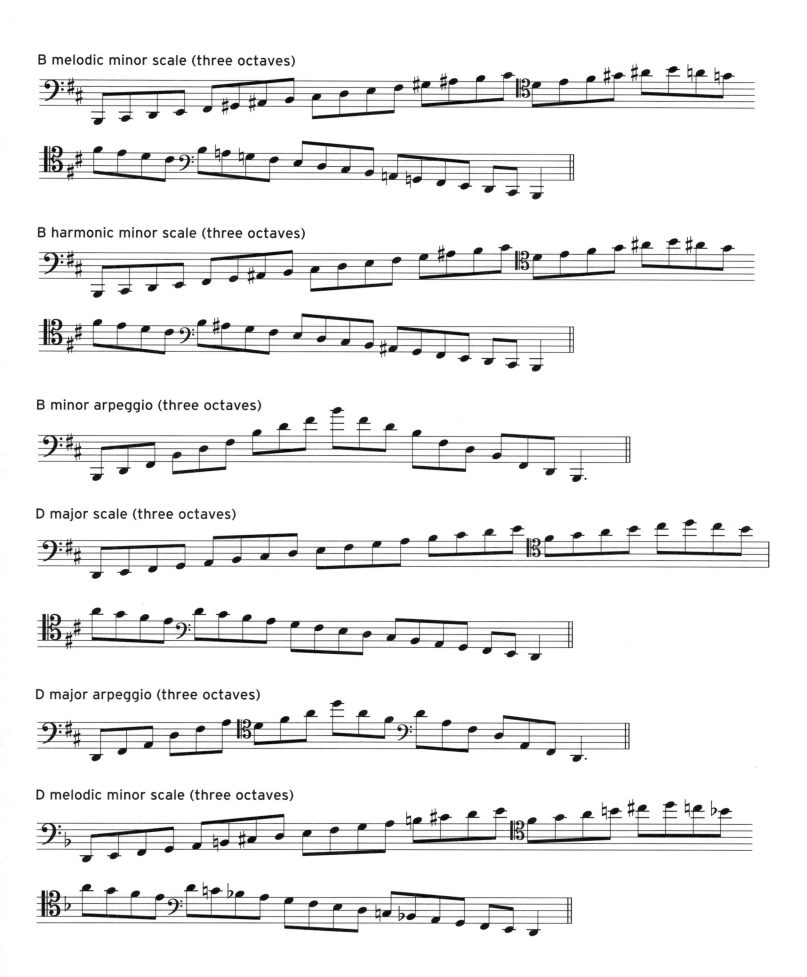

B harmonic minor scale (three octaves)

B minor arpeggio (three octaves)

D major scale (three octaves)

D major arpeggio (three octaves)

D melodic minor scale (three octaves)

Grade 8 continued

D harmonic minor scale (three octaves)

D minor arpeggio (three octaves)

F# major scale (two octaves)

F# major arpeggio (two octaves)

F# melodic minor scale (two octaves) – see Grade 5 page 21

F# harmonic minor scale (two octaves) – see Grade 5 page 20

F# minor arpeggio (two octaves) – see Grade 5 page 21

E major scale (two octaves) – see Grade 5 page 20

E major arpeggio (two octaves) – see Grade 5 page 20

E melodic minor scale (two octaves)

E harmonic minor scale (two octaves)

E minor arpeggio (two octaves)

A♭ major scale (two octaves) – see Grade 4 page 13

A♭ major arpeggio (two octaves) – see Grade 4 page 13

G♯ melodic minor scale (two octaves)

G♯ harmonic minor scale (two octaves)

G♯ minor arpeggio (two octaves)

Chromatic scale starting on D (three octaves)

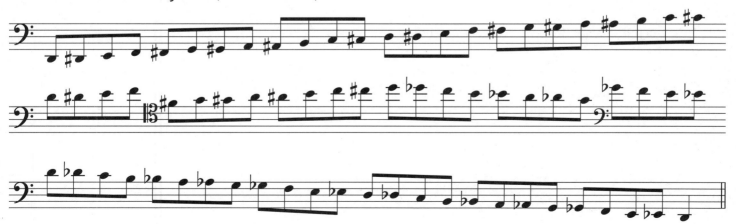

Grade 8 continued

Dominant 7th in the key of G (three octaves)

Whole-tone scale starting on B (two octaves)

Pentatonic (major) scale starting on B (two octaves)

Dominant 7th in the key of B (two octaves)

Diminished 7th starting on B (two octaves)

Diminished 7th starting on F# (two octaves)

Augmented arpeggio starting on F# (two octaves)

Augmented arpeggio starting on A♭ (two octaves)